Pocket Puzzlers: Brain Teasers

10 9 8 7 6 5 4 3

Published by Sterling Publishing Company, Inc.
387 Park Avenue South, New York, N.Y. 10016

Material in this collection was adapted from
Classic Brainteasers © Martin Gardener
Brain Bafflers © Robert Steinwachs
Great Book of Mind Teasers & Mind Puzzlers © George J. Summers
Mind-Sharpening Lateral Thinking Puzzles © Edward J. Harshman

Distributed in Canada by Sterling Piublishing
c/o Canadian Manda Group, One Atlantic Avenue, Suite 105
Toronto, Ontario, Canada M6K 3E7
Distributed in Australia by Capricorn Link (Australia) Pty Ltd
P.O. Box 6651, Baulkham Hills, Business Centre, NSW 2153, Australia
Manufactured in the United States of America.

Pocket Puzzlers: Brain Teasers

Martin Gardner
Robert Steinwachs
George J. Summers
Edward J. Harshman

Sterling Publishing Co., Inc. New York

Contents

Brain Bafflers

Answers on pages 71–76

Warm up on a Few Easy Ones

1. How many of each kind of animal did Moses take on the Ark?

2. How many apples would you have if you took two apples from three apples?

3. If a billion follows a million and a trillion follows a billion, what number follows a trillion?

4. Gus and Joe are raising pigs. Gus said that if Joe would give him two pigs they would have an equal number, but if Gus gave Joe two of his, Joe would have twice as many as Gus. How many pigs did they each have?

5. How many months have twenty-eight days?

6. Is it legal for a man to marry his widow's sister?

7. If you had to swallow one pill every half hour, how much time would it take for you to swallow three pills?

8. What day would yesterday be if Thursday was four days before the day after tomorrow?

9. How should you pronounce the second day of the week: Tee-use-day or Twos-dee?

10. Counting one number per second twenty-four hours per day, how long would it take to count to a billion? A trillion?

11. Write down the number eleven thousand, eleven hundred, and eleven.

12. What is it you sit on, sleep in, and brush your teeth with?

13. Write in what every good citizen should do on election day. __ __ __ __

14. If Mama bull, Papa Bull, and Baby Bull are in the pasture and Baby Bull gets scared, who would he run to?

15. Which number follows ten thousand ninety-five?

Ten thousand ninety-seven?
Ten thousand ninety-nine?

16. Without using the dictionary, how is “polo-pony” pronounced?

17. In the spaces in the box, place the numbers 1 through 16 without any consecutive number touching.

18. A man can paint a room in four hours, and another man can paint the same room in two hours. How long would it take to paint the room if they worked together?

19. Can you make four equilateral triangles with six toothpicks?

20. A dog had three puppies, named Mopsy, Topsy and Spot. What was the mother's name?

21. A microbe doubles itself every second, and in one minute it fills a jar. How long would it take to fill the same jar if you started with four microbes?

22. A boy and a girl born on the same day of the same year with the same parents are not twins. How is this possible?

23. Divide twenty by one-half and add three. What is your answer?

24. It is a scientific fact that a person eats over an inch of dirt at every meal. How is this possible?

25. What is the least number of queens that could be used to command an entire chessboard?

26. Is the Great Wall of China ten miles long? One hundred miles long? A thousand miles long? Two thousand miles? More?

27. Will and Jim were practicing shooting, and each scored seventy-five hits out of a hundred. After a little break, Will tried again and hit thirty-five out of fifty shots. Jim did not do any more shooting. Who had the best average for the day?

28. Two half-mile sections of steel railroad track were laid and absolutely secured on each end. The sun expands the steel one foot (12 inches). Now the overall length is 5,281 feet, and since it is secured at the ends it will buckle in the middle. How high from the ground will it buckle?

29. A pipe can fill a tank with water in thirty minutes. A larger pipe can fill the tank in twenty minutes, and a still-larger pipe can fill it in ten minutes. How long would it take to fill the tank if all three were opened at once?

Classic Brain Teasers

Answers on pages 74–76

Open-and-Shut Case

Mrs. Higgenbotham has opened the shutters to let in fresh air through the window. The artist has made a curious mistake. Can you spot it?

Two Customers

A person who was unable to hear entered a stationery store to buy a wall pencil sharpener. To make the clerk understand what he wanted, he poked a finger into his left ear and then made a grinding motion around his other ear with his fist. The clerk understood at once.

A man who was unable to see now entered the store. How did he make the clerk understand that he wanted to buy a pair of scissors?

Name the Product

CUSTOMER: How much is one?
CLERK: Thirty cents.
CUSTOMER: I'll take fourteen.
CLERK: Sixty cents.
CUSTOMER: I'll take a hundred and forty-four.
CLERK: That will be ninety cents.
What on earth is the customer buying?

The Pistol Duel

A century ago, two Frenchmen, Alphonse and Gaston, fought a duel with pistols. Each put a bullet through his opponent's head, yet neither Alphonse nor Gaston died. How could this be?

Mrs. Perkins' Pets

All of Mrs. Perkins' pets are dogs except one, and all her pets are cats except one. How many cats and dogs does she have?

The Stolen Lugs

Mr. Green has removed a flat tire and is putting on the spare. He doesn't know that a squirrel is stealing the four lugs (nuts) that hold the tire to the axle. After finding the lugs missing, how does Mr. Green manage to attach his spare tire and drive to the nearest service station where he can obtain four more lugs?

Donald Gets His Roller Blades

Donald lived with his parents and an older sister in a one-story brick house on the end of Main Street. One afternoon the doorbell rang. Donald opened the door. It was his friend Tommy, who lived across the street.

"Let's go skating," said Tommy.

"Okay," Donald said. "Wait there until I get my roller blades."

Donald ran quickly up the stairs. He got his skates from under the bed in his room on the second floor. Then he ran outside and put them on. He and Tommy spent the rest of the afternoon skating.

What's wrong with this story?

Who Reads Faster?

If it takes Willie 80 minutes to read a short story, and it takes his sister an hour and ten minutes to read the same story, who is the faster reader?

Ripping Good Puzzle

If you were to tear pages 8, 9, 48, 53, and 54 out of this book, how many separate sheets of paper would you rip out?

A Knotty Problem

Can you figure out a way to hold a piece of rope or string, one end in each hand, and tie a knot in the string without letting go of either end?

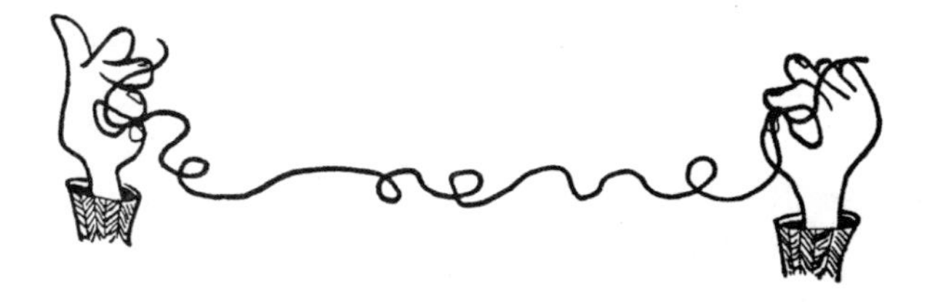

The Amazing Computer

A store has on sale a computer and word processor small enough to fit in your pocket. It can add, multiply, subtract, divide, and write in all languages. A delete device will correct any error: No electricity is required to operate it. The price? Only a few cents! How can the store make a profit by selling it so cheap?

Professor Egghead's Proverbs

Professor J. Fortescue Egghead likes to use big words and complicated sentences. Here is how the professor would say eight well-known proverbs. See how many you can recognize, and then check the answers on pages 75 to 76.

A rotating fragment of mineral collects no bryophytic plants.

Exercise your visual faculties prior to executing a jump.

Under no circumstances compute the number of your barnyard fowl previous to their incubation.

An excess of individuals skilled in the preparation of edibles impairs the quality of thin soup.

A feathered biped in the terminal part of the arm equals in value a pair of feathered bipeds in densely branched shrubbery.

A recently purchased implement for brushing away floor dirt invariably effaces the dirt most efficiently.

A timorous heart at no time succeeds in aquiring the beautiful damsel.

Everything is legitimate in matters pertaining to ardent affection and armed conflict between nations.

How Comes

1. A truck driver went three blocks the wrong way down a one-way street without breaking the law. How come?

2. A boy and a girl are standing on the same sheet of newspaper, yet it is impossible for them to kiss. How come?

3. Thirty people died in a plane crash, but not a single survivor was buried. How come?

4. A cowboy rode into Dodge City or Friday, stayed two days, then rode out of town on Friday. How come?

5. A man tossed a soccer ball ten feet. It stopped in midair, reversed direction and came back to him. How come?

6. There are only two Rs in "Robert Richardson." How come?

7. A dog trotted all the way across a lake without sinking in the water. How come?

8. A prizefighter was unconscious seven times during the same week, yet he was never ill or injured or knocked out in a fight. How come?

9. A person living in Oklahoma can't be buried in Texas. How come?

10. A snooper was able to see right through the brick wall of a house. How come?

11. A lady took her poodle for a walk. The dog did not walk ahead of her, behind her, or on one side. How come?

12 A man married 57 women. None died, and he was never divorced, yet he was one of the most admired men in town. How come?

Name the Men

Mr. Cook, Mr. Sailor, and Mr. Carpenter met on the street one afternoon.

"Isn't it funny," said Mr. Cook to the others, "that not one of us has a profession that is the same as our names?"

"That's true," agreed the man who was the carpenter.

Can you now give the correct last name of each man shown in the picture below?

Hint: Since Mr. Cook is talking to the carpenter, he cannot be the carpenter.

Mind Teasers

Solution Schemes on pages 35–42
Answers on pages 77–84

Speaking of Children

"We—Aaron, Brian and Clyde—each have some children.

1. Aaron has at least one girl and twice as many boys as girls.

2. Brian has at least one girl and three times as many boys as girls.

3. Clyde has at least one girl and three more boys than girls.

4. When I tell you the number of children we have altogether—a number less than 25—you will know how many children I have, but not how many children each of the others have. Altogether we have ..."

Who is the speaker?

Card Games

Althea, Blythe, and Cheryl played some card games, each game having exactly one winner.

1. No player won two games in succession.

2. When a player was the dealer for a game, she did not win that game.

3. The deal proceeded from Althea to Blythe to Cheryl; then this order was repeated until they stopped playing.

4. The only player to win more than two games did not win the first game.

Who was the only player to win more than two games?

Fathers and Sons

Statement A:
Both fathers always tell the truth
or both fathers always lie.

Statement B:
One son always tells the truth
and one son always lies.

Statement C:
Statement A and statement B are not both lies.

Of the statements above and the men who made them:

1. Gregory made one of the statements, his father made another of the statements, and his son made the remaining statement.

2. Each father and son mentioned in the statements refers to one of the three men.

3. Each man either always tells the truth or always lies.

Which statement—A, B, or C—was made by Gregory?

The Tennis Players

Zita, her brother, her daughter, and her son are tennis players. As a game of doubles is about to begin:

1. Zita's brother is directly across the net from her daughter.

2. Her son is diagonally across the net from the worst player's sibling.

3. The best player and the worst player are on the same side of the net.

Who is the best player?

Relations

Lee, Dale and Terry are related to each other.

1. Among the three are Lee's legal spouse, Dale's sibling, and Terry's sister-in-law.

2. Lee's legal spouse and Dale's sibling are of the same sex.

Who do you know is a married man?

After-Dinner Drink

Abigail, Bridget, and Claudia often eat dinner out.

1. Each orders either coffee or tea after dinner.

2. If Abigail orders coffee, then Bridget orders the drink that Claudia orders.

3. If Bridget orders coffee, then Abigail orders the drink that Claudia doesn't order.

4. If Claudia orders tea, then Abigail orders the drink that Bridget orders.

Who do you know always orders the same drink after dinner?

My Secret Word

One of the words listed below is my secret word.

AIM DUE MOD OAT TIE

With this list in front of you, if I were to tell you any one letter of my secret word, then you would be able to tell me the number of vowels in my secret word.

Which word is my secret word?

Equal Sums

A B C
D
E F G
H
I

Each of the digits 1,2,3,4,5,6,7,8 and 9 is:

1. Represented by a different letter in the figure above.

2. Positioned in the figure above so that each of A+B+C, C+D+E, E+F+G, and G+H+I is equal to 13.

Which digit does E represent?

Solution Schemes

Speaking of Children

Orientation

Some trial and error is necessary in solving this puzzle.

Solution Scheme

Make a chart for yourself as follows:

Total number of children: _____
Possible numbers of children had by:

Aaron	Brian	Clyde

Write a number in the blank and three numbers in each row of the table in as many ways as possible—crossing off any unused boxes—so that no condition is contradicted.

Card Games

SOLUTION SCHEME

Make a chart for yourself as follows:

Dealer	A	B	C	A	B	C	A	B	C
Winner									

Using A,B, and C for the women, write a letter in each box–crossing off any unused boxes—so that no condition is contradicted.

Fathers and Sons

Orientation

Gregory is the only one of the three who is both a father and a son.

Solution Scheme

Make a chart for yourself as follows:

Statement A	
Statement B	
Statement C	

Write "true" or "false" for each statement so that no condition is contradicted and so that the truth or falseness of each man's statement is not contradicted.

The Tennis Players

ORIENTATION

Certain arrangements of four players on a tennis court are identical, though they appear to be different at first glance.

For example,

W	X
Z	Y

is identical to

Y	Z
X	W

because a rotation of one arrangement results in the other.

SOLUTION SCHEME

Make a diagram for yourself as follows:

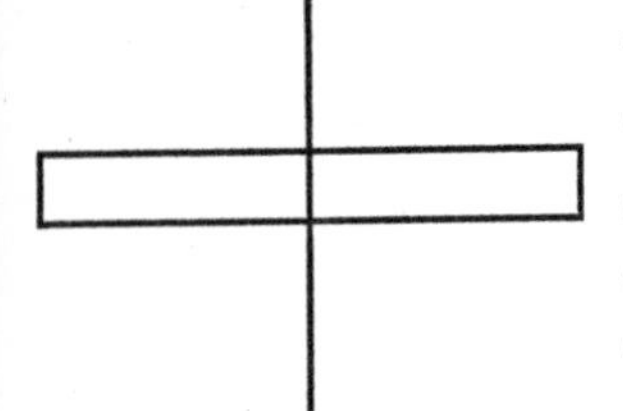

Write "Zita," "brother," "daughter," or "son" in each part of the tennis-court diagram so that no condition is contradicted.

Relations

ORIENTATION

A person's sister-in-law may be the sister of that person's spouse or the wife of that person's brother.

SOLUTION SCHEME

Make a chart for yourself as follows:

Lee's spouse Sex M / F	Dale's sibling Sex M / F	Terry's sister-in-law Sex M / F

Write "Lee," "Dale," or "Terry" in each box and indicate the sex of each person so that no condition is contradicted.

After-Dinner Drink

ORIENTATION

From "If X orders milk, then Y orders milk" and "X orders milk," the only possible conclusion is "Y orders milk." From "If X orders milk, then Y orders milk" and "Y orders milk," more than one conclusion is possible: either "X orders milk" or "X does not order milk."

SOLUTION SCHEME

Make a chart for yourself as follows:

Abigail orders	Bridget orders	Claudia orders

Write "coffee" or "tea" in each box in as many ways as possible—crossing off any unused boxes—so that no condition is contradicted.

My Secret Word

Orientation

"Any" in the second sentence enables you to determine my secret word.

Solution Scheme

Make a chart for yourself as follows:

A	D	E	I	M	O	T	U

Write "no" under each of the letters which cannot be in my secret word according to the condition given in the second sentence.

Discussion

There are 256 possible ways that "no" could be written in the table. It is wise, then, to eliminate as many cases as possible, using the one "clue," before listing those remaining cases which involve more extended reasoning. Indeed, it turns out that only one case need be listed.

The Orientation tells the reader how to use the "clue." In other words, the "clue" says that *each* letter of my secret word is contained only in words having the same number of vowels. So M, for example, cannot be in my secret word because it is in AIM which has two vowels and in MOD which has only one vowel.

Equal Sums

ORIENTATION
A, B, C, and D are respectively and simultaneously interchangeable with I, H, G, and F; only E can be determined with certainty. Each of A,B,D,F,H and I occurs in only one sum; each of C, E, and G occurs in two sums.

SOLUTION SCHEME
Make a diagram for yourself as follows.

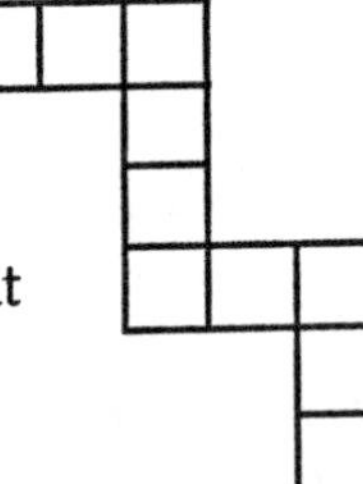

Write a digit in each box so that no condition is contradicted.

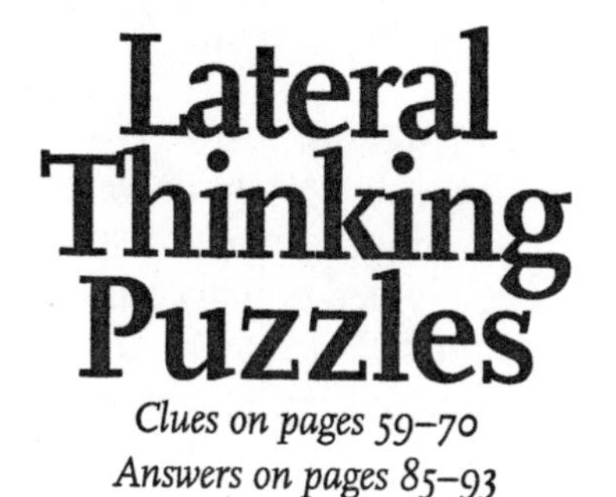

Clues on pages 59–70
Answers on pages 85–93

How Can This Be?

A Gift to Share

Laura won a prize in a fund-raising raffle. It had been donated by a local business, a women's clothing store. "Great!" she exclaimed happily, on hearing of her win. "I know just the person to share it with!" What was it?

The Will

A man died, leaving four grown children. His will left one-fifth of his estate to be divided equally among all law-abiding male offspring, three-fifths of it to be divided equally among all female offspring, and the balance to be divided equally among his grandchildren. His offspring were Pat, Leslie, Terry, and Evelyn. Pat had joined the Navy. Leslie gained local notoriety for getting many women pregnant. Terry got a job in a hospital and married a nurse. Evelyn had been convicted of murder and was in prison. After the estate was settled, Evelyn's son had inherited exactly twice as much as anyone else. Explain.

Half-Jaundiced

Jaundice is a sign of liver impairment that makes the whites of a person's eyes, and the skin of a Caucasian person, turn yellow. One hospital patient had a jaundiced appearance in one eye, but not the other. Why?

Ski Through the Tree

The tracks of two skis were visible in the otherwise virgin snow. They led directly to a tree, then the tracks passed the tree—one on each side of it! How were the tracks made?

Short Swing

Ned, a Little League baseball player, watched the coach open a large box and take out several baseball bats. "That's a big box," said Ned to the coach. "It has to be," replied the coach, "to hold several bats." "Not really," said Ned. "We have a box at home that holds about a dozen and it's only half that size." Does Ned know what he's talking about?

The Switch of Mastery

The family was sitting around, reading and relaxing. "This monster is great! He's master of all he surveys," said little Matthew, looking up from a comic book. "If I flip this switch," replied his mother, "*we* will be master of all *we* survey." How?

He's All Wet

A man stood outdoors under an umbrella. It was a large umbrella, large enough to cover him completely; and there was no wind. He was not standing in a pond or other body of water. So why was he thoroughly drenched?

Safe Landing

Vic, a seven-year-old boy, was in the park with his mother. He climbed to the top of a hundred-foot tree. Then his mother called him. "Vic, come here!" she shouted. He jumped from the top of the tree, landed uninjured on the ground, and ran to his unconcerned mother. How did he land without hurting himself?

No Sale

A telephone solicitor, trying to sell magazine subscriptions, dialed a number chosen at random from the phone book. Instead of the intended recipient, the solicitor reached the circulation manager for the magazine. The telephone solicitor was dialing carefully and did not want to call the circulation manager, but kept reaching the manager anyway, even after trying the number several times. Explain.

Spoken by the Book

After a singularly dull lecture that followed a formal dinner, a man walked up to the lecturer and said, "Strikingly unoriginal. I have a book that has every word of your speech in it, and most people here do, too." The lecturer was enraged and demanded proof. He got it. How?

Trials of the Uninvited

John was making lunch when his friend Ron arrived, unexpectedly bringing along his two kids and their nanny. Soon, the men, unconcerned, were sitting in the kitchen eating steak sandwiches, while the kids, unfed, played outside under their nanny's watchful eye. When the hungry kids started to chew on strands of grass, the nanny didn't stop them. Why not?

Daffy Decisions

Strong Enough Already

Willie entered an exercise program, and when he finished it his right arm was more than a hundred times stronger than when he had started. He told his friend Spike, a boxer, about this great improvement and the program. Spike thanked Willie for the information, but he was not interested in taking part in the program. Why not?

Self-Destruction

One approach to reducing health care costs is to discourage self-destructive behavior. Smoking, driving without seat belts, and certain other activities are identified as needlessly risky; and social pressure has built to make them less and less desirable. One form of self-destructive behavior, however, receives little public attention. It can lead to reconstructive surgery, but people who receive the surgery often do not stop the behavior and need the surgery again. Oddly enough, the health care administration establishment itself is biased against having this particular self-destructive behavior identified as such. What is it, and why does the health-administration establishment not want it recognized?

No Place for Women

High-heeled shoes, girdles, stockings, and other articles of women's clothing have been attacked as the result of a male-dominated society. What characteristic of some women's clothing boutiques can be similarly attacked?

Tricky Tactics

Rainy Walk

Ima Burred Breyne lived in a suburban development and had two parrots. She enjoyed walking in sunny weather, and her parrots enjoyed sunlight too. But she took them outside only during heavy rain. Why?

Scared Mother

A young mother wheeled her baby, in a carriage, through a park. A man looked at the baby and admired it. "What a lovely baby," he said. "Thank you," she replied, smiling gently. A few minutes later, a woman saw the baby and gushed, "What a beautiful boy! I'd love to take him home with me." The mother screamed, snatched up the baby and ran. Why?

Zelda Was Cured

Zelda, who had a one-month-old baby, was five feet eight inches tall. Although she told her doctor about suffering low-back pain, the doctor simply blamed it on the loose ligaments resulting from childbirth and was not very helpful. When she told her husband about it, he promptly did something that greatly reduced her pain and required neither drugs nor exercise. What did the husband do?

The Upside-Down Newspaper

A timid-looking man sat on a bench in a city park. He held a newspaper upside down and was reading intently. Why?

She Cheated

A history teacher gave an essay test. To one question, two students, Sherry and Mary, gave identical answers. Their handwriting gave no clue as to who had copied from whom. Nevertheless, the teacher found Mary guilty of cheating. How?

Mowing the Pool

Helen had an in-ground swimming pool with a narrow deck and small lawn next to her home. The pool and lawn were encircled by tall trees which provided privacy. Every week over the summer months, her son first mowed the lawn; then he pushed the lawn mower around the concrete deck that surrounded the pool, although no grass grew there. Why?

He Held His Liquor

Randy and Andy were at a table in the back of a bar, each holding a bottle of beer. They finished their beer, and Andy got up and walked over to the bartender. He returned with two full beer bottles, handed one to Randy, and sat down. Again, they drank until their bottles were empty. Again, Andy walked over to the bartender and returned with two full bottles. They repeated this process until they had each finished about ten bottlefuls. Randy was, predictably, drunk. Why was Andy nearly sober?

Picking Good Apples

Cora, Flora and Nora went for a walk in the woods and encountered a tall apple tree. It had wonderful ripe apples; but someone must have been there just before them, for all of the good apples were too high for them to reach. Some worm-infested apples could be easily picked, and more bad apples lay on the ground. How did the ladies gather some good apples?

Tied Up in Knots

You have two ropes, a thick one and a thin one. You want to tie one rope to the other one. If the ropes were the same size, or similar in size, you would be able to use any of several knots to connect them. Their differing bulk is a problem, but fortunately not an insurmountable one. How do you do it?

Tiresome Questions

Two suburban neighbors stood, talking, at the small fence that separated their lots. "How tall is your son now?" asked Marla. "He keeps growing, of course." replied Carla, "and I can't really say; but this morning he stood next to my husband's new truck and was just as tall as its right front tire." "How tall is that?" continued Marla. Carla shook her head. "I don't know. My husband's gone now with the truck, and I can't even tell you what kind it is," replied Carla. Marla wandered around the fence and up Carla's driveway, then asked Carla to lend her something. Soon, both of them knew how tall Carla's son was. How did Marla figure it out?

Recycle the Envelope

Prudence sent a letter to a friend of hers, who lived across the country. The letter asked for the return of the envelope, nothing more. Why did she do this?

Clues

How Can This Be?

Ski Through the Tree

Q: Was the tree tall and rigid, not a knee-high sapling that could be skied over?
A: Yes.
Q: Were there ski-pole prints or footprints near the tree showing that the skier removed one ski, or any lightening of either ski track there?
A: No.
Q: Were both tracks made by one expert skier?
A: Yes.

The Will

Q: Were Pat, Leslie, and Terry all law-abiding?
A: Yes.
Q: Did Evelyn's son have any siblings or cousins?
A: No.
Q: Was Leslie paid for getting the women pregnant?
A: Yes.

A Gift to Share

Q: Were two or more separately-chosen prizes wrapped together?

A: No

Q: Was it an ensemble of jewelry or other such set often broken up into two or more items and generally considered useful alone?

A: No.

Q: Was half of the prize completely useless to Laura?

A: Yes.

Half-Jaundiced

Q: Diagnosing the cause of jaundice in a particular patient requires special medical skill, but can this particular question be answered without it?

A: Yes.

Q. Could the answer be inferred by examining the patient's eyes?

A: Yes.

Q: When a bright light shines on a normal person's eyes, the pupils constrict equally. Would this patient's pupils do so?

A: No.

Short Swing

Q: Can Ned's box really hold at least a dozen bats?
A: Yes.
Q: Does it have a lid that opens and closes?
A: No.
Q: Is it designed to be moved from place to place?
A: No.

The Switch of Mastery

Q: Was the mother telling the truth?
A: Yes.
Q: Were there other buildings within a half mile or so?
A: No.
Q: Was the approximate time of day important?
A: Yes.

He's All Wet

Q: Were other people, who stood nearby or walked past the man with the umbrella, wet?
A: No.
Q: Was it raining?

A:No.
Q: Had the umbrella been altered?
A: Yes.

Safe Landing

Q: Did Vic land on ordinary hard ground, not in water or on a trampoline or other cushioning object?
A: Yes.
Q: Did his mother fear for his safety?
A: No.
Q: When he jumped from the top of the tree, did he fall less than a hundred feet?
A: Yes.

No Sale

Q: Was there something wrong with the telephone, the telephone wiring, or the number that the solicitor dialed?
A: No.
Q: Was the solution to the problem known to the person whose number was dialed?
A: Yes.
Q: Could the intended recipient of the call have

only one telephone number in the household or office?
A: No.

Spoken by the Book

Q: Had the lecturer plagiarized from something widely in print or otherwise well known to the entire audience?
A: No.
Q: Did the book contain material that the lecturer did not use?
A: Yes
Q: Did the words of the lecture appear in the book in the same order that they were used in the lecture?
A: No.

Trials of the Uninvited

Q: Was anyone upset at the kids' actions?
A: No.
Q: Did the kids' complain?
A: No.
Q: Did they usually eat grass?
A: Yes.

Daffy Decisions

Strong Enough Already

Q: Was Spike rational in not wanting to enter the program?

A: Yes.

Q: Was the program intended for athletes?

A: No.

Q: When Willie finished the program, was his arm stronger than it was six months before he started it?

A: No.

Self-Destruction

Q: Has health care administration traditionally been a woman's job?

A: Yes.

Q:In an office setting, is an ambitious woman under pressure to dress elegantly?

A: Yes.

Q: Does the self-destructive behavior have to do with women's clothing?

A: Yes.

No Place for Women

Q: Is it the attitude of the sales staff or a fault in the store's floor plan (cramped dressing rooms, etc.)?
A: No.
Q: Does it concern the merchandise offered rather than any particular article of clothing?
A: Yes.
Q: Is the placement of the merchandise inconvenient?
A: Yes.

Tricky Tactics

Rainy Walk

Q: Did Ms. Breyne's parrot especially enjoy rain?
A: No.
Q: Were they restrained by a cage or leash when outside?
A: No.
Q: Could they fly?
A: Yes.

Scared Mother

Q: Did anyone display a weapon or otherwise

threaten the mother?
A: No.
Q: Did the woman resemble anyone who had previously threatened the mother?
A: No.
Q: Had something very unpleasant happened to the mother and her baby?
A: Yes.

Zelda Was Cured

Q: Did Zelda, like many new mothers, often pick up and hold her baby?
A: Yes.
Q: Was her husband taller than her?
A: Yes.
Q: Did Zelda's husband also like to pick up and hold the baby?
A: Yes.

The Upside-Down Newspaper

Q: Was the upside-down newspaper a signal to anyone, perhaps a coded message from one spy to another or an attention-getting mannerism to provoke a friendly conversation from a stranger?

A: No.
Q: The man was reading, but was he reading the newspaper?
A: No.
Q: Did the man know that the newspaper was upside down?
A: No.

She Cheated

Q: Other than noting that Sherry and Mary had sat next to each other, had the teacher noted anything suspicious as they took the test?
A: No.
Q: Had the teacher graded other essay tests from those same students?
A: Yes.
Q: Did Sherry have a perfect mastery of English grammar?
A: No.

Mowing the Pool

Q: Was the son trying to lengthen the time spent doing the job, perhaps because he was paid by the hour?

A: No.
Q:Was the mower's engine running while he pushed the mower around the pool?
A: Yes.
Q: Are the trees significant?
A: Yes.

He Held His Liquor

Q: Did Andy drink from his bottle, not pour beer on the floor or into a hidden container?
A: Yes.
Q: Did Andy have an unusual tolerance for alcohol?
A: No.
Q: When Andy went for more drinks, did he order two beers?
A: No.

Picking Good Apples

Q:Did Cora, Flora, and Nora shake or climb the tree?
A:No.
Q: Did they prop a fallen branch against a branch of the tree and shake the branch?

A: No.
Q: Would ripe apples fall from the tree after only a minor disturbance?
A: Yes.

Tied Up in Knots

Q: Do you use a particular kind of knot, such as a sheet bend, known to work if the rope sizes aren't too different?
A: No.
Q: Do you unwind and attach strands of the ropes, or use strong glue, tape, or other fastening material?
A: No.
Q: Is the answer to knot one rope first?
A: Yes.

Tiresome Questions

Q: Did Marla ask for any information about the truck or its tire size?
A: No.
Q: Was the new truck ever driven on an unpaved surface?
A: Yes

Q: Was Carla's driveway paved?
A: No.

Recycle the Envelope

Q: Did Prudence use an unusual stamp and want it canceled and returned?
A: No.
Q: Is it significant that the letter was sent to a distant part of the country?
A: Yes.
Q: Did she have access to a fancy copier, one that could handle odd sizes and thicknesses of paper, including envelopes?
A: Yes.

The Answers

Brain Bafflers

Page 7.

1. Moses? Noah was the captain of the Ark.
2. Two apples, of course.
3. One trillion and one.

Page 8.

4. Gus had ten pigs, Joe had fourteen pigs.
5. All twelve months have 28 days.
6. No, he would be dead!
7. One hour—for instance, if you swallowed one at 7:00, one at 7:30, and one at 8:00.
8. Friday.
9. The second day of the week is pronounced Mon-day!

10. Approximately 3.2 years to count to a mere billion, and about 3,200 years to count to a trillion.

11. 12,111.

page 9

12. A chair, a bed, and a toothbrush.

13. If you printed and did not write the word, you are wrong.

14. Whoever heard of a Mama Bull?

Page 10.

15. 10,096; 10,098; 10,100.

16. Polo pony. (You ride it when you play polo!)

17.

1	9	2	10
3	11	4	12
5	13	6	14
7	15	8	16

Page 11.

18. 80 minutes.

19. Make a pyramid out of the six toothpicks.

20. "What."

Page 12.

21. 58 seconds.

22. Two out of a set of triplets.

23. 43.
24. There is at least an inch of dirt under the chair a person is sitting on (it may be under the floorboards, but it's there).

Page 13.

25. Five queens.
26. Over 3,000 miles long.

Page 14.

27. Jim's average is higher.
28. Over 55 feet.
29. A bit over 5 1/2 minutes.

Classic Brain Teasers

Open-and-Shut Case
Slats slant opposite ways on opposite sides of a shutter. In this picture, the slats slant the same way on both sides.

Two Customers
The man said to the clerk, "I want to buy a pair of scissors."

Name the Product
The customer is buying house numbers.

The Pistol Duel
Alphonse and Gaston did not duel each other.

Mrs. Perkins' Pets
Mrs. Perkins has one cat and one dog.

The Stolen Lugs
Mr. Green removed one lug from each of the other three tires and used them to attach the spare. Three lugs will hold a tire firmly enough for a short drive.

Donald Gets His Roller Blades
Donald lived in a one-story house, so he couldn't have had a bedroom on the second floor.

Who Reads Faster?
Willie's sister is the faster reader. She finished the story in 70 minutes, which is ten minutes less than Willie's 80 minutes.

Ripping Good Puzzle
Four. Pages 53 and 54 are two sides of the same sheet.

A Knotty Problem
Cross your arms before you seize the ends of the string. Uncross your arms and it will tie a knot in the cord.

The Amazing Computer
The computer is a wooden pencil with an eraser.

Professor Egghead's Proverbs
1. A rolling stone gathers no moss.
2. Look before you leap.
3. Never count your chickens before they hatch.
4. Too many cooks spoil the broth.
5. A bird in the hand is worth two in the bush.

6. A new broom sweeps clean.
7. Faint heart ne'er won fair lady.
8. All's fair in love and war.

How Comes

1. The truck driver was on foot.
2. They were standing on opposite sides of a door.
3. Survivors are not dead.
4. Friday was the name of the cowboy's horse.
5. He tossed the soccer ball straight up in the air.
6. The other two r's in Robert Richardson are lower case.
7. The lake was frozen.
8. The prizefighter was asleep in bed seven times.
9. He isn't dead
10. The snooper looked through a window.
11. The poodle walked on the other side.
12. The man was a minister.

Name the Men

Mr. Cook couldn't be the cook, nor could he be the carpenter, because the carpenter replied to his question. So he must be the sailor. Mr. Carpenter can't be the carpenter or the sailor, so he must be the cook. This leaves Mr. Sailor; who must be the carpenter.

Mind Teasers

Speaking of Children

From [1], Aaron has at least 3 children and a number of children from this sequence:

3, 6, 9, 12, 15, 18, 21, 24, ...

From [2], Brian has at least 4 children and a number of children from this sequence:

4, 8, 12, 16, 20, 24, ...

From [3], Clyde has at least 5 children and a number of children from this sequence:

5, 7, 9, 11, 13, 15, 17, 19, 21, 23, ...

Then the total number of children is at least 12 and, from [4], at most 24. Also: If the total number of children is even, Aaron must have an odd number of children; if the total number of children is odd, Aaron must have an even number of children.

Trial and error reveals the following information. The total number of children cannot be 13 because no three numbers, one from each sequence, can total 13. The total cannot be 12,14, 15, 16, or 17 because then the number of children each had would be known, contradicting [4]. The total cannot be 18, 20, 21, 22, 23, or 24 because then no number of children could be known for anybody, contradicting [4]. So the total is 19.

When the total is 19, Aaron must have an even number of children and, from the sequences, this number must not be greater than 19–(4+5) or 10. So Aaron must have 6 children. Then Brian and Clyde together must have 13 children. Then Brian must have either 4 or 8 children. Then: if Brian has 4 children, Clyde has 9 children; if Brian has 8 children, Clyde has 5 children.

So *the speaker is Aaron.*

Card Games

Let A represent Althea, B represent Blythe, and C represent Cheryl. Then, from [1] and [2], the possible sequence of wins is as follows:

Dealers, from [3]	A	B	C	A	B	C	A	B
Case I	C*	A	B	C	A	B	C	–
Case II	B	A*	B	C	A	B	–	–
Case III	B	C	B*	C	A	B	–	–
Case IV	B	C	A	C*	A	B	C	–
Case V	B	C	A	B	A*	B	–	–
Case VI	B	C	A	B	C	B*	–	–
Case VII	B	C	A	B	C	A	C*	–
Case VIII	B	C	A	B	C	A	B	–

From [4], listing continues until one player wins three games. (Each asterisk indicates the point where the rest of a sequence is determined; one deal earlier a choice between two players is possible. Each succeeding case represents the other choice for the preceding case.) From [4], Cases I, II, III, V, VI, and VIII are eliminated. So Case IV or VII is the right one. In either case, *Cheryl was the only player to win more than two games.*

Fathers and Sons

If statement C is false, statement A and statement B are both false. But—from [1], [2], and [3]—if statement A is false, statement B or statement C is true (because a false statement A implies one father always tells the truth and one father always lies). So statement C cannot be false and must be true.

Because statement C is true, at least one of statements A and B is true. But—from [1] and [2]—if statement B is true, statement A or statement C is false. So if statement B is true, statement A is false.

In summary:

	Case I	Case II
Statement A	true	false
Statement B	false	true
Staement C	true	true

If Case I were the right one, then—from statement A and from [2]—the speakers of statements A and C would both be fathers; and—from statement B and from [2] and [3]—the speakers of statements A and C would both be sons (because a false statement B implies both sons always tell the truth or both sons always lie). This situation is impossible from [1] because only Gregory is both a father and a son; so Case I is eliminated.

Then Case II is the right one. Then, from statement A and from [2] and [3], the speaker of statement A is a father; and, from statement B and from [2], the speaker of statement A is a son. So, from [1], Gregory made statement A.

The Tennis Players

From [1], the players must be relatively positioned in one of the following ways:

daughter	son
brother	Zita

Ia

daughter	Zita
brother	son

Ib

son	daughter
Zita	brother

IIa

Zita	daughter
son	brother

IIb

Then, from [2]: For ways Ia and IIa	For ways Ib and IIb
Brother is the worst player's sibling. Zita is the worst player.	Daughter is the worst player's sibling. Son is the worst player.

Then, from [3]: For ways Ia and IIa	For ways Ib and IIb
Brother is the best player.	Brother is the best player.

So, in any case, *Zita's brother is the best player.*

After-Dinner Drink

From [1] and [2] there are six possibilities:

	Abigail orders	Bridget orders	Claudia orders
Case I	coffee	coffee	coffee
Case II	coffee	tea	tea
Case III	tea	coffee	coffee
Case IV	tea	tea	tea
Case V	tea	coffee	tea
Case VI	tea	tea	coffee

Then, from [3], Cases I and V are eliminated and, from [4], Cases II and V are eliminated. *So you know Abigail always orders the same drink* (tea) *after dinner.*

My Secret Word

From the "clue": If you were told any one of the letters in MOD, then you would not be able to determine whether the number of vowels in my secret word is one or two. So none of the letters in MOD is in my secret word. Then my secret word cannot be AIM, DUE, MOD, or OAT. *So my secret word is TIE.*

Relations

From [1]:

If Lee's spouse is Dale, then Dale's sibling cannot be Lee and must be Terry; then Terry's sister-in-law cannot be Dale and must be Lee.

If Lee's spouse is Terry, then Terry's sister-in-law cannot be Lee and must be Dale; then Dale's sibling cannot be Terry and must be Lee.

Then, in any case, all three of Lee, Dale, and Terry are accounted for and Terry's sister-in-law is a female.

So, from [2], Lee's spouse and Dale's sibling are both males.

In summary:

	Lee's spouse	Dale's sibling	Terry's sister-in-law
	male	male	female
Case I	Dale	Terry	Lee
Case II	Terry	Lee	Dale

Case II is eliminated because Lee and Terry cannot both be males and married to each other. So Case I is the correct one and you know *Dale is a married man.* Lee is a married woman, Dale and Terry are brothers, and Lee is Terry's sister-in-law.

Equal Sums

One digit must be 9. Then, from [1] and [2], 9 must go with 1 and 3. One digit must be 8. Then, from (1) and [2], 8 must go with either 1 and 4 or 2 and 3. One digit must be 7. Then, from [1] and [2], 7 must go with either 1 and 5 or 2 and 4. One digit must be 6. Then, from [1] and [2], 6 must go with either 2 and 5 or 3 and 4.

From the diagram no digit may be used in more than two sums. From this and the fact that 9 goes with 1 and 3:

Case I. If 8 goes with 1 and 4, then 7 goes with 2 and 4; then 6 goes with 2 and 5.

Case II. If 8 goes with 2 and 3, then 6 goes with 2 and 5; then 7 goes with 1 and 5.

But Case II is impossible because the digit 4 does not occur. So Case I is correct and, from the diagram, *E must be 4.*

```
        9  3  1

              8

              4  7  2

                    5

                    6
```

A possible arrangement of the digits is shown here.

Lateral Puzzles

How Can This Be?

A Gift to Share

Laura had earlier lost an arm in an accident, and the prize she won was an expensive pair of leather gloves. She knew a woman with one arm, the opposite arm, who had the same glove size, and she planned to give this friend the glove that she herself could not use.

The Will

Pat, Leslie, and Terry were women. Leslie worked in a fertility clinic and outraged local religious extremists. Terry married a male nurse. Evelyn, the only son, was not law-abiding and inherited nothing. The estate went 1/5 each to Pat, Leslie, and Terry and 2/5 to Evelyn's son.

Half-Jaundiced

The patient had a glass eye.

Ski Through the Tree

The expert skier, familiar with parallel skiing (in which the skis are kept parallel at all times), could ski while wearing only one ski. He made the tracks on two different runs, first passing the tree on one side and then passing it on the other.

Short Swing

Ned's parents, to control insects, have a box not for baseball bats but for the flying mammals. A suitably designed box, open at the bottom and permanently mounted, encourages bats to move in.

The Switch of Mastery

Late at night, in a rural area without nearby neighbors or street lights, the mother could turn off the main light switch and effect complete darkness. Then, they would all be master of all they survey because they could not survey, or see, anything.

He's All Wet

The man was a charity volunteer. He had attached small rubber tubes to the umbrella ribs, pierced the tubes with a needle, and connected the tubes to a water source. Now, stationed at a shopping mall, he was deliberately keeping himself wet, seeking donations for flood victims.

Safe Landing
The tree had been recently uprooted by a tornado, and it lay sideways on the ground. The top was only about ten feet from the ground, and Vic hung from it before jumping.

No Sale
Irritated at receiving telephone solicitations, one recipient of them decided to retaliate. He used a caller-ID device to identify the name and phone number of incoming calls. If it was a magazine salesperson, instead of answering the phone he quickly dialed the magazine's circulation department, using a second telephone line, and connected the two lines together. Neither the solicitor nor the circulation manager could easily figure out what was happening, and the manager received the full effect of the nuisance calls.

Spoken by the Book
The book was an unabridged dictionary.

Trials of the Uninvited
The nanny and kids were goats, and Ron was trying to convince John to buy them from him to keep John's lawn trimmed.

Daffy Decisions

Strong Enough Already

Willie had had a stroke that temporarily paralyzed his arm. Rehabilitative exercises and neurologic recovery helped him regain some, but not all, of his arm strength.

Self Destruction

Women sometimes tend to wear tight-fitting or high-heeled shoes that can lead to hammertoes or bunions. Health administrators, many of whom rationally decide to wear visually attractive shoes, notwithstanding the drawbacks, collectively resist having corrective foot surgery be declared an uninsurable expense, as this would put them at personal material risk.

No Place for Women

Tall people, obviously including tall women, can easily reach high racks or shelves out of reach of shorter people. Conversely, short women can more easily reach shelves nearer the floor than can tall women. Common sense would suggest putting tall sizes on higher shelves or racks and petite sizes on lower ones, but stores often do exactly the opposite. Such a practice may cause a tall woman to have to bend sharply forward, presenting a needlessly awkward display, and force a short woman to request hands-on help when seeking clothing in her size that is out of her reach.

Tricky Tactics

Rainy Walk

Ima did not want her parrots to fly out of her reach, which parrots can do if full-flighted and taken outside. Heavy rain would wet her parrots' wings and make them incapable of flight, and Ima knew that they could be taken out safely under her umbrella. They would stay dry if they remained with her, but they would be forced to flutter to the ground if they left her.

Scared Mother

The baby, soon after being born, had been kidnapped and almost given, with a forged birth certificate and adoption papers, to a childless couple who wanted a son. Police intervened and restored the baby to the young mother. Still afraid of losing her baby to the couple, she made it a point to dress the boy in colors that didn't denote his sex.

Zelda Was Cured

Her husband lengthened the legs of the crib so that the baby could be picked up more easily, without its parents bending so low. The constant bending, especially when the back and pelvic ligaments have become loosened for childbirth, strains the back muscles. Raising the height of the crib reduces the need for bending, a detail often ignored by many obstetricians.

The Upside-Down Newspaper

The man was a recent immigrant who did not read English, so didn't realize that the paper he was holding was upside down. As he did not want to be recognized as a foreigner, but enjoyed sitting outside in the park, he was reading his native-language book behind the newspaper, hoping that no one would notice.

She Cheated

The teacher recalled from Sherry's earlier essays, and from the current one, that she confused "its" with "it's." The question in dispute, with both answers identical, included a few misuses of "its' and "it's." Mary used those two words correctly in all her other work, so she must have copied Sherry's answer, errors and all.

Mowing the Pool

Leaves falling from the trees would land on the pool deck. The draft from the mower was strong enough to push those leaves away from the pool, so that they would not be blown into it. Using the lawn mower as a blower was faster than raking the leaves.

He Held His Liquor

Andy, after the first beer, ordered one beer and one serving of soda whenever he walked over to the bartender. He had become tired of being accused of unwillingness to drink heavily, and the bartender cooperated by pouring the soda into Andy's empty beer bottle in return for a good tip.

Picking Good Apples

The bad apples were not good to eat, but they were available and easily thrown. The ladies merely threw the bad apples at the clusters of good apples and knocked plenty of good apples to the ground.

Tied Up in Knots

Fasten one rope end to itself, making a loop, then pass the other rope through the loop and knot it to itself. Interlocking bowline knots are commonly used to fasten odd-sized ropes together.

Tiresome Questions

Marla could easily see tire tracks that the new truck had made. She hoped to find, and did, that a small pebble had got stuck in a tire tread. The pebble made a mark on the ground at intervals that matched the tire's circumference. Marla borrowed a tape measure and measured the distance between the pebble marks to learn the circumference of the truck tire, then divided it by 3.14 to calculate the boy's height.

Recycle the Envelope

The United States Postal Service puts a series of vertical lines (a bar code) on the bottom of ordinary-sized first-class envelopes. These lines permit them to be sorted by machine. Prudence knew that putting a bar code for a distant part of the country on an envelope would significantly delay its delivery. When mailing a check from an interest-bearing account, when the date of postmark is considered more important than the date of delivery, the delay permits additional interest to be earned and can be well worth the effort of copying the bar code onto the envelope.

Index